Information for Parents

In literacy lessons teachers will be seeking to encourage their pupils to:

• Read confidently and with understanding;
• Understand phonics and spelling patterns;
• Use neat handwriting with speed and accuracy;
• Expand their vocabulary;
• Appreciate a range of styles in fiction and poetry;
• Understand how stories are structured by the writers' use of settings, characters and plots;
• Read and use non-fiction materials;
• Develop their own writing using techniques of planning, drafting and editing;
• Enjoy reading books;
• Use imagination and inventiveness in their own writing.

Throughout the primary years the children will address their literacy work in two broad areas:

(i) Speaking and listening, through discussion, interaction and drama;

(ii) Reading and writing for a range of purposes on paper and on computer screen.

You can provide support to your children in the first of these areas by giving them lots of opportunities to speak to other people and to listen carefully in a range of situations.

Using the books in this **Literacy Now** series will give your children a wealth of extra support in the second area: reading and writing.

Through the series we provide practice materials for reading words and spelling them, understanding and responding to texts, developing well-structured sentences and using a range of punctuation correctly and effectively.

The books are matched appropriately to ages and are designed to be used by parents working with their children to provide extra practice, whether out of a need to improve particular aspects of English or simply for the fun of working on the subject at home.

Lite for ages 5–6

Excellent practice for literacy

Your child will enjoy working through this book alongside you. Most children will need help reading the short passages of writing and answering the questions. You may like to read the passages to your child. This will help her/him to gain confidence.

The experience of reading and writing with one-to-one support will be of enormous value to your child and will help to build solid foundations for her/his education.

Andrew Brodie

1

An apple tree

Use words from the box to label this picture.

bird   grass
tree   apple
nest   flower

Now follow the instructions to colour the picture.
You will find them on the next page.

An apple tree

Colour the grass green.

Colour the apples red.

Colour the flowers pink and yellow.

Colour the leaves green.

Colour the tree trunk brown.

Colour the bird blue.

In, on, over, under

Look at the pictures to complete the sentences.
Use these words: in   on   over   under

The bird is _ _ _ _ the tree.   The doll is _ _ the box.

The cat is _ _ _ _ _ the chair.   The jug is _ _ the table.

A busy room

Label
the picture.

Use words
from the box.

door cat dog
picture chair
light table

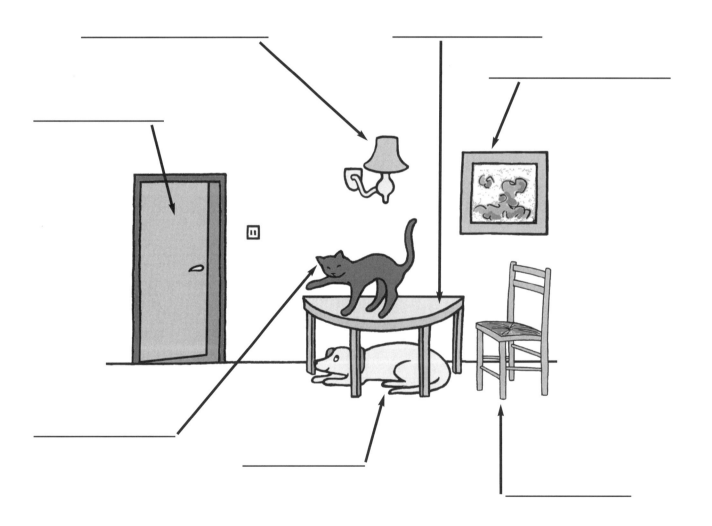

A busy room

Now fill in the missing words.

1. The _ _ _ is on the _ _ _ _ _.

2. The _ _ _ is under the table.

3. The _ _ _ _ _ is beside the _ _ _ _ _.

4. A _ _ _ _ _ _ _ is on the wall.

5. The _ _ _ _ is open.

6. The _ _ _ _ _ is above the table.

Draw pictures to match the labels.

A cat under a table

A dog beside the door

5

Rhyming words

Enjoy reading this counting rhyme.

One, two, three, four, five,
Once I caught a fish alive.
Six, seven, eight, nine, ten,
Then I let it go again.

Why did you let it go?
Because it bit my finger so.
Which finger did it bite?
This little finger on the right.

**Choose the word from the poem that
rhymes with each of the following words.**

five ⟶ _____

again ⟶ _____

so ⟶ _____

bite ⟶ _____

Rhyming words

Look at these words.

Join the words that rhyme.

The first one has been done for you.

bell	say
rain	pan
day	red
me	pain
bed	tea
man	fell

Learn to spell these number words.

Look at each one, then write it twice.

one _____ _____   two _____ _____

three _____ _____   four _____ _____

five _____ _____   six _____ _____

seven _____ _____   eight _____ _____

nine _____ _____   ten _____ _____

Missing words

Each sentence has lost a word.
The missing words are in the box.
Put the words in the correct places.

> playing   house
> little   three   two
> because   water   dig

1 I saw _ _ _ girls
eating ice creams.

2

The boy was _ _ _ _ _ _ _ _
with a large red ball.

3

_ _ _ _ _ _ birds sat in the tree.

8

Missing words

4 I wash with soap and
_ _ _ _ _ _ every day.

5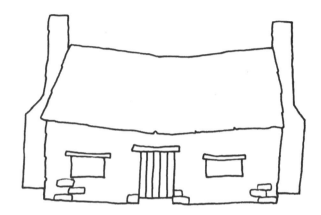

The old _ _ _ _ _ _
had two chimneys.

6 I like school _ _ _ _ _ _ _ _
I can play with my
friends there.

7 I like to _ _ _ holes on
the beach.

8

A _ _ _ _ _ _ _ mouse ran across the carpet.

9

Doctor Foster

Doctor Foster went to Gloucester
In a shower of rain.
He stepped in a puddle,
Right up to his middle,
And never went there again.

Please answer the questions on the next page.

Doctor Foster

Put a ring around the correct answer for each question.

1 'Doctor Foster' is a ...

        story   poem   song

2 Where did Doctor Foster go?

      to a puddle   to town   to Gloucester

3 What did he step in?

    a paddle   a puddle   the street   a pond

4 Did he go to Gloucester again?

    never   sometimes   always   every week

5 Which word in the poem rhymes with rain?

    Gloucester   puddle   middle   again

Now write the poem in your very best handwriting.

_____

_____

_____

_____

Three little pigs

Little Pig One had a house of straw.
The big bad wolf came through the door.

Little Pig Two had a house of sticks.
The big bad wolf was up to his tricks.

Little Pig Three had a house of bricks.
Wolf soon found himself in a fix!

Now ring the correct answers.

1 In the straw house the wolf went in ...

through the window   down the chimney

through the door   through a hole

Three little pigs

2 Little Pig Three lived in a house made of ...

stone   sticks   straw   bricks

3 How many pigs are in the poem?

one   two   three   four

4 What sort of house did Little Pig Two live in?

a stone house   a straw house

a stick house   a brick house

Name the animals in the pictures.
Use words from the box.
Then you can colour the pictures.

bird	pig
wolf	cow
cat	dog

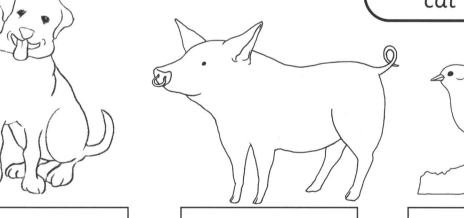

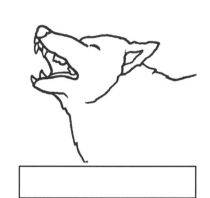

Front and back covers

Front cover

Pet Care

by I.M. Furry

Write the answers to these questions.

1 What is the title of the book?

_____

2 What is the name of the author?

_____

3 Do you think this is a story book?

_____

4 Do you think it is an information book?

_____

Front and back covers

Back cover

Pet Care by I.M. Furry

● All you need to know about looking after pets.

● 20 different sorts of pets included.

● More than 50 coloured pictures included.

● Caring for sick pets.

Andrew Brodie Publications

Ring the correct answers.

1 How many coloured pictures are in the book?

twenty   fifty   more than fifty

2 Can this book help if your pet is ill?

yes   no

3 Could you learn about trees in the book?

yes   no

Write the correct answers.

4 What is the name of the publisher of the book? _____

5 How many different sorts of pet are in the book? _____

Foxes

Foxes live in towns and in the countryside. They eat many different things. In towns they will take food scraps from bins. Foxes hunt for their food at night.

A fox has a thick bushy tail called a brush. It has a pointed nose or snout and large ears.

Most foxes are a reddish brown colour; these are called red foxes. In the very cold area near the North Pole there are white foxes; these are called arctic foxes.

Use words from the box to label the picture.

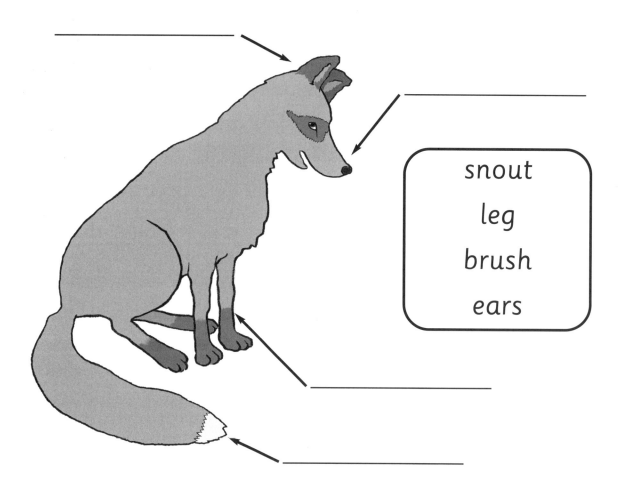

snout

leg

brush

ears

Foxes

Now write answers to these questions.

1 What colour are arctic foxes?

_____

2 What might a fox look for in a dustbin?

_____

3 When do foxes go out to hunt for food?

_____

4 What is the name given to the tail of a fox?

_____

5 Which part of the fox is its snout?

_____

6 What sort of fox lives near the North Pole?

_____

7 What colour is a red fox?

_____

The friendly monster

Mig was a friendly monster.

She lived inside a cave in a mountain.

Mig was green and yellow with three blue eyes and four pink feet.

Mig lived with her two pets dogs called Zim and Zam.

Ring the correct answers.

1 Mig had ...

green feet   pink feet

yellow feet   blue feet

2 Mig had ...

two eyes   three eyes

one eye   four eyes

3 Where did Mig live?

with her pets   inside a cave

in a house   with four dogs

The friendly monster

Write the correct answers.

4 Write the names of Mig's pet dogs.

_____   _____

5 How many feet did Mig have?

_____

Draw a picture of Mig.

Picture word matching

Write the correct word under each pet picture.

| cat | dog | bird | rabbit |

_____   _____   _____   _____

19

Sing a song of sixpence

Sing a song of sixpence,
A pocket full of rye;
Four and twenty blackbirds
Baked in a pie!
When the pie was opened
The birds began to sing;
Wasn't that a dainty dish
To set before the king?

The king was in his counting house,
Counting out his money;
The queen was in the parlour,
Eating bread and honey.
The maid was in the garden
Hanging out the clothes
When down came a blackbird
And pecked off her nose.

Ring the correct answers.

1 Where were the blackbirds?

In a pocket   In a pie

In the parlour   In the counting house

2 What was the queen doing?

eating pie   hanging out the washing

eating bread and honey   counting money

Sing a song of sixpence

3 What did the birds do when the pie was opened?

they began to sing   they flew away

they counted money   they ate the pie

4 How many blackbirds were baked in the pie?

forty-two   forty-four

twenty-four   twenty-two

Write the answers.

5 What was the king doing in his counting house?

_____

6 What did a blackbird do to the maid?

_____

Alphabetical order

Use the letters from the box to complete the alphabet.

a   w   f   n
s   k   z

_ b c d e _ g h i j _ l m _ o p q r _ t u v _ x y _

Now copy the alphabet carefully.

_ _

The Easter fair

It was Easter and the fair had come to town. All the rides and stalls were set up in the market place.

Jill and Joe were very excited as Mum and Dad said they would take them to the fair on Saturday.

Jill wanted to ride on the galloping horses. She liked the way they moved up and down while they were going round.

Joe wanted to go on the dodgem cars and the big wheel.

Now answer the questions.

Ring the correct answers.

1 What time of year was it?

Christmas   New Year   Easter

2 What had come to town?

The fair   the market place   Easter

3 Who were very excited?

Jill and Dad   Joe and Mum

Mum and Dad   Joe and Dad

Joe and Jill   Jill and Mum.

4 When were the family going to the fair?

Monday   Tuesday   Wednesday

Thursday   Friday   Saturday   Sunday

Write the answers to these questions.

5 What did Jill want to ride on?

_____

_____

_____

6 What did Joe want to go on?

_____

_____

_____

Waiting for the bus

Sal and Mum were at the bus stop. They were waiting to catch the bus into town. Sal liked to look at all the other people waiting too.

There was an old lady with a walking stick, an old man, two big girls and three big boys.

Sal counted carefully. There were nine people waiting altogether.

At last the big red bus came along. Sal and Mum climbed on and sat down. Soon they would be in town at the shops.

Ring the correct answers.

1 Why were Sal and Mum at the bus stop?

They were waiting to catch a train.
They were waiting to catch a bus.
They were waiting to count people.

2 Who had a walking stick?

Mum   an old man

Sal   an old lady

3 How many people were at the bus stop?

    none   seven

        nine   ten

4 What sort of bus came along?

  a big red bus   a big blue bus

    a small blue bus   a small red bus

5 Why were Sal and Mum going to town?

   to visit the museum   to visit the bus stop

  to visit the shops   to visit the swimming pool

Write the correct word under each picture.

bus   van   bicycle   lorry   tractor   car

_____

_____

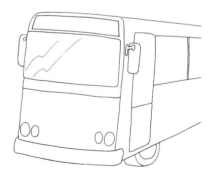
_____

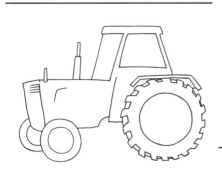
_____

_____

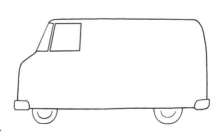
_____

Doctors

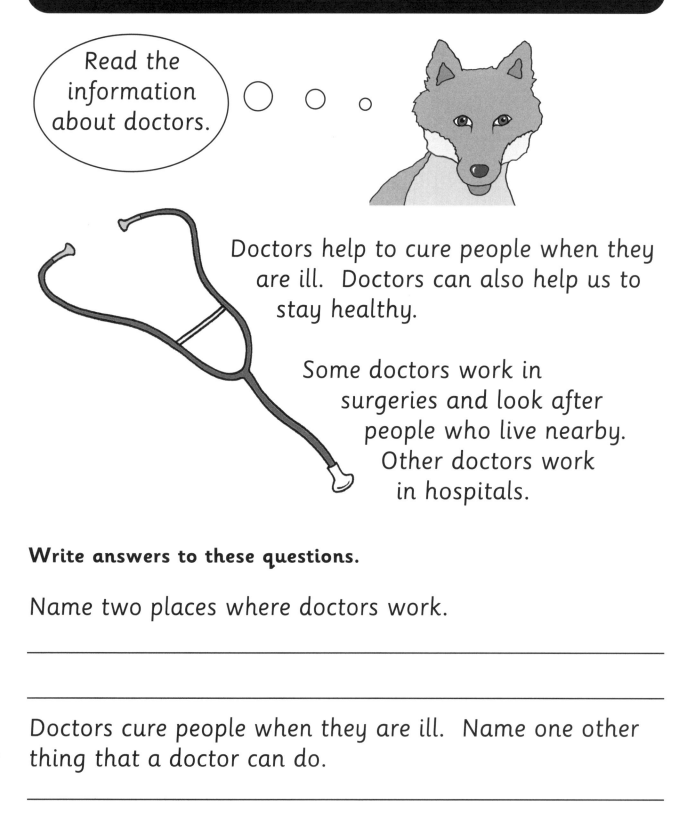

Read the
information
about doctors.

Doctors help to cure people when they
are ill. Doctors can also help us to
stay healthy.

Some doctors work in
surgeries and look after
people who live nearby.
Other doctors work
in hospitals.

Write answers to these questions.

Name two places where doctors work.

_____

_____

Doctors cure people when they are ill. Name one other
thing that a doctor can do.

_____

_____

Do doctors look after pets, people or wild animals?

_____

_____

Doctors

Look at the words in the box.

> nearby   healthy
>
> hospitals   cure

Write the correct word next to each of the meanings below.

To make an ill person well again: _____

To be feeling fit and well: _____

Somewhere close: _____

Place where ill people can be looked after: _____

Draw your doctor here.

Colour your picture.

The airport

Mum and Dad took Jon to the airport. They were going to meet Jon's granny and grandad. Granny and Grandad had been on holiday. Jon was excited, as he loved going to the airport.

The airport was very busy. Jon held Dad's hand tightly, as he didn't want to get lost.

Mum and Dad took Jon to a café where they had a drink. The café had a large window so Jon could watch the planes taking off and landing. Jon wished he could go on a plane.

Soon it was time for Granny and Grandad's plane to land.

Mum, Dad and Jon stood with a crowd of people. Dad picked Jon up so he could see better.

Suddenly Jon saw Granny and Grandad. He was pleased to see them.

They all went back to Jon's house where Granny and Grandad told him all about their holiday.

Ring the correct answers.

1 Who took Jon to the airport?

Granny and Grandad   Mum and Dad

Dad and Grandad

2 How did Jon feel about going to the airport?

excited   sad

tired   pleased

The airport

3 Who had been on holiday?

Jon   Mum and Dad

Granny and Grandad

Write the answers to the questions.

4 What did Jon wish he could do?

_____

5 Why did Jon hold Dad's hand?

_____

6 What two things did Jon do in the cafe?

_____

_____

Muddled sentences

My sentences are in a muddle! Please write them correctly. Remember to start each sentence with a capital letter and finish with a full stop.

I like toast. cheese on

_____

chimney. comes out of a Smoke

_____

the river. swam in The fish

_____

Jamal visits the doctor

Jamal woke on Monday morning feeling ill. His ear hurt.

Mum took Jamal to the surgery so that the doctor could look into Jamal's ear.

The doctor used a special torch to see inside Jamal's sore ear.

"Oh dear," said the doctor, "Jamal's ear looks very sore. I will give him some medicine that will make it better."

Jamal and Mum went home with the medicine. Jamal had to take one spoonful after each meal.

Very soon Jamal was feeling well again. He was glad the doctor had helped him.

Put a ring around the correct answers.

1 Which part of Jamal was hurting?

    his eye   his ear   his arm   his leg

2 On what day of the week did Jamal need to go to see the doctor?

    Monday   Tuesday   Wednesday   Thursday

    Friday   Saturday   Sunday

3 What did the doctor give to Jamal to make him feel better?

some tablets   a torch   some medicine

4 When did Jamal have to take his medicine?

once a week   after each meal   after breakfast

The letters oo or ee are missing from the words below. Complete the words and colour the pictures.

tr_ _   b_ _ k   sch _ _ l

thr_ _   m_ _ n   sh_ _ p

31

a e i o u

These letters are called vowels.

Write the correct vowel in each word.

m _ t

c _ p

b _ n

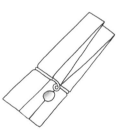

p _ g

p _ t

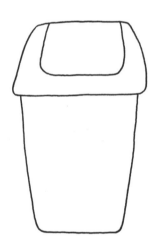

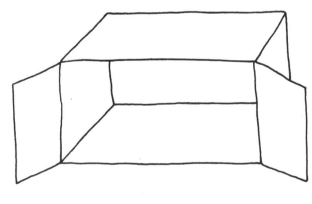

b _ x

m _ g